RAE Revision Notes

George Benbow, G3HB

Radio Society of Great Britain

Published by the Radio Society of Great Britain, Cranborne Road, Potters Bar, Herts EN6 3JE.

First published 1971
Second edition 1993

ISBN 1 872309 18 6

Cover design: Geoff Korten Design.
Cover photo: Thomas Neile Photographers in association with ICOM (UK) Ltd.
Illustrations: Derek Cole, Radio Society of Great Britain.
Production and typography: Ray Eckersley, Seven Stars Publishing.

Printed in Great Britain by Bell & Bain Ltd, Glasgow.

CONTENTS

1. BASIC THEORY AND CIRCUITS

An electric current is a movement of electrons from one atom to another of a particular substance. This movement is caused by the application of voltage. The substance, generally in the form of a wire, is known as a 'conductor' of electricity. When the voltage applied comes from a battery, the electric current flows in one direction only; this is a 'direct' current, created by the application of a 'direct' voltage.

The direction of the current flow is said to be from the positive terminal of the battery to the negative terminal. This is the 'conventional' current.

Some substances will not conduct electricity, ie electrons cannot be detached from their atoms. These are known as 'insulators'.

    Common conductors: copper, silver, aluminium.
    Common insulators: plastics, ceramics, mica.

The flow of an electric current is opposed by a property of the conductor known as 'resistance'. A 'resistor' is a discrete component manufactured to have a particular value of resistance.

Ohm's Law

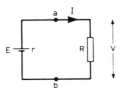

The ratio of voltage (in volts) applied across a resistor to the current (in amps) which flows through the resistor is constant.

$$\frac{V}{I} = \text{constant}$$

This constant is the resistance of the resistor. It is measured in ohms.

$$\frac{V}{I} = R \qquad \frac{\text{volts}}{\text{amps}} = \text{ohms}$$

Note that the current I also flows through the battery, hence there is a voltage drop across the battery.

Power

A current flowing through a resistor causes heat to be dissipated in that resistor. Power thus dissipated is:

Power (watts) = voltage (volts) × current (amps)

From Ohm's Law power is also expressed as:

$$W = V^2/R \qquad \text{and} \qquad W = I^2 \times R$$

Alternating currents

Voltage and current vary smoothly and regularly between equal positive and negative maxima (a sinusoidal waveform or sine wave), ie they are not constant. The characteristics of a sine wave are shown below.

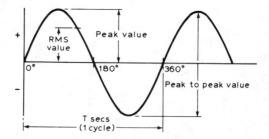

RMS (root mean square) value

Voltage which is equivalent in heating effect to a direct supply of the same voltage. For a sine wave, it is 0.707 times the peak value.

Average value

Average value is 0.636 times the peak value.

Frequency

The number of complete cycles per second (one cycle per second is 1 hertz, abbreviated to '1Hz')

$$f = \frac{1}{T} \qquad\qquad T = \frac{1}{f}$$

Phase difference between waveforms

Phase difference is measured in degrees – one cycle is said to be 360°.

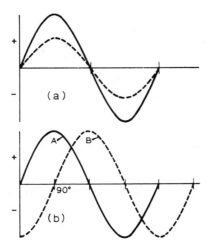

(a) Two waveforms 'in phase', ie they start at the same time.
(b) Two waveforms with phase difference of 90°. A 'leads' B by 90° and B 'lags' on A by 90°.

Distortion

Distortion of an alternating waveform is caused by the presence of other waveforms which have frequencies related to the original or 'fundamental' frequency (f). A frequency of $2f$ is the second harmonic, $3f$ is the third harmonic, and so on. The amount of distortion also depends on the phase of the harmonics present.

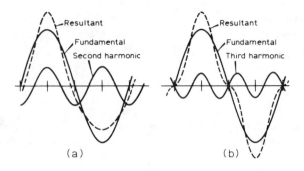

(a)　　　　　　　　　　(b)

Magnetism

All iron is weakly magnetic, and the resultant magnetic field attracts other pieces of iron. The strongest field is at the ends: the 'north pole' (ie the north-seeking pole) and 'south pole' (ie south-seeking pole). These are so named because, if freely suspended, a bar of iron comes to rest pointing at the earth's magnetic poles.

Permanent magnets are made of alloys of iron with nickel, cobalt or aluminium, and they produce very strong fields. Their uses in radio include loudspeakers, headphones, moving-coil meters etc.

A magnetic field is created by a current passing through a wire. It can be enhanced by winding the wire into a coil and more so by introducing an iron core into the coil. This is an 'electromagnet' which has north and south poles just like a permanent magnet. These poles are reversed if the current is reversed.

Inductance

Self-inductance

If a steady current flows through a conductor, it will create a steady magnetic field around the conductor. A current change will tend to alter the strength of the field, which in turn will induce in the conductor a voltage ('back EMF') which tends to oppose the change. This process is called 'self-induction' and the wire is said to have 'self-inductance', usually abbreviated to 'inductance'. The unit of inductance is the henry (H), and one henry develops a back EMF of 1V when the current changes at a rate of 1A per second.

Inductance is increased significantly by winding the conductor in the form of a coil and much more so by introducing a core of magnetic material into the coil. Inductance depends on the number of turns, area and the relative permeability (μ_r) of the material within the coil ($\mu_r = 1$ for air and up to 2000 for magnetic materials).

The range of inductance encountered in radio is from about one microhenry (1µH) to at least 20 henrys (20H).

Mutual inductance

A changing current in one circuit can induce a voltage in a second circuit. The magnitude of the voltage induced depends upon the tightness of the coupling between the circuits. The two coils are said to have a mutual inductance of one henry when, if the current in the primary coil changes at a ratio of 1A/s, the voltage across the secondary is one volt. The symbol for mutual inductance is M.

Capacitance

The capacitance of a conductor or a body is the ratio of its charge (Q) to its potential (V). In most cases this capacitance is extremely low. A device in which this effect is enhanced is called a 'capacitor'. The electric field concentrated between two parallel plates can be much more intense without raising the potential excessively.

The capacitance of a parallel-plate capacitor is proportional to the area of the plates and the 'relative permittivity' of the material (the 'dielectric') between the plates, and inversely proportional to the distance between the plates. Common dielectrics are air, paper, plastics (polycarbonate, polyester etc), mica and ceramics having permittivities of 1, 2, 3–5, 5 and 10 upwards respectively.

The unit of capacitance is the farad (F). A charge of one coulomb on the capacitance of one farad would raise the potential to one volt. The farad is an extremely large unit; capacitances are usually measured in microfarads or picofarads. The range of capacitance in radio work is 1pF to at least 60,000µF.

Reactance (X)

Reactance is the opposition to the flow of an alternating current offered by inductance or capacitance.

Inductive reactance (X_L)

$$X_L = 2\pi f L$$

(X_L is in ohms when f is in hertz and L in henrys.)

Capacitive reactance (X_C)

$$X_C = \frac{1}{2\pi f C}$$

(X_C is in ohms when f is in hertz and C in farads.)

When an alternating voltage is applied to a resistor, the resultant current is in step or in phase with the voltage. Ohm's Law applies. In the case of an inductor, the current flowing lags behind the applied voltage by 90°. In the case of a capacitor, the current leads the applied voltage by 90°. Current which flows is:

$$I_L = \frac{V}{X_L} \quad \text{and} \quad I_C = \frac{V}{X_C} \quad \text{respectively}$$

Effective reactance

In a circuit containing L and C effective reactance is ($X_L - X_C$) or ($X_C - X_L$) according to whichever is larger.

Impedance

Total opposition to the flow of an alternating current, taking resistance into account, is the impedance (Z), made up of R and X. Both are measured in ohms but they must not be added arithmetically. Because of the 90° phase shift introduced by inductance and capacitance, they must be added by taking the square root of the sum of the squares of R and X.

$$Z = \sqrt{R^2 + X^2}$$

Ohm's Law now applies, ie

$$Z = \frac{V}{I}$$

Tuned circuits

A capacitor and an inductor can be connected in parallel (a) or in series (b) to form a tuned circuit.

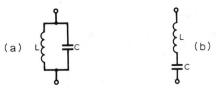

At one frequency, X_L will be equal to X_C. This is the 'resonant frequency'.

$$X_L = X_C$$

or

$$2\pi f L = \frac{1}{2\pi f C}$$

hence

$$f = \frac{1}{2\pi\sqrt{LC}}$$

(f is in hertz when L is in henrys and C in farads.)

The impedance of a series-tuned circuit is a minimum at resonance, hence it is called an 'acceptor' circuit as it accepts maximum current at resonance. Impedance is equal to the effective resistance of the circuit.

The impedance of a parallel-tuned circuit is a maximum at resonance, hence it is called a 'rejector' circuit as it rejects current at resonance.

Q – magnification factor of tuned circuit

The current which flows in a parallel-tuned circuit at resonance (the 'circulating current') is increased or magnified by a factor generally known as the 'Q of the tuned circuit'.

$$Q = \frac{\omega L}{R} \quad (\omega = 2\pi f)$$

Losses in the capacitor are usually low, so the Q is determined by the inductor. The range of Q is roughly 100–400 depending on the form of the inductor.

In series-tuned circuits it is the voltages across L and C which are magnified by the factor Q.

Dynamic resistance (R_D)

Dynamic resistance is the impedance of a parallel tuned circuit at resonance.

$$R_D = \frac{L}{CR} \quad \text{Since } Q = \frac{\omega L}{R}, \quad R_D = \frac{Q}{\omega C}$$

L/C ratio

Resonant frequency depends on $L \times C$, hence infinite range of L and C is theoretically possible. 'Stray' capacitance of circuit layout (10–20pF) determines minimum capacitance. Compromise value in a tuned circuit is about 1.5pF per metre of wavelength.

Resonance (or selectivity) curve

Shows the response of a tuned circuit at frequencies above and below resonance. The 'bandwidth' is the width of this curve (in kilohertz) at a particular level (eg level at which response is 0.707 times the maximum, the half-power point).

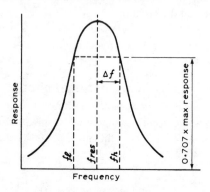

Relationship between Q and bandwidth is:

$$Q = \frac{f_r}{f_h - f_l} = \frac{f_r}{2\Delta f}$$

For a given Q, the lower f is, the lower Δf is, ie bandwidth is less and selectivity is greater. Similarly, bandwidth is inversely proportional to Q.

Overall bandwidth is reduced, particularly in the 'skirts' of the frequency response, by several tuned circuits in cascade.

Bandwidth is increased by a 'damping' resistor across a tuned circuit.

Coupled circuits

The response of two coupled tuned circuits depends upon the degree of coupling between them and also on their Q. Response for different degrees of coupling is shown below:

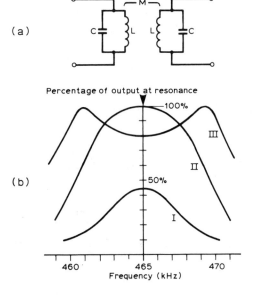

(a)

(b)

Percentage of output at resonance

Transformers

The basis of transformer action is a voltage induced in one winding by a changing current in another winding tightly coupled to the first winding. Transformers are therefore AC devices.

Transformer relationships

Turns ratio is the number of turns on the primary (n_p) and secondary (n_s) winding, ie ratio is n_p/n_s

hence
$$V_s = \frac{n_s}{n_p} \times V_p \quad \text{or} \quad \frac{V_s}{V_p} = \frac{n_s}{n_p}$$

similarly
$$I_p = \frac{n_s}{n_p} \times I_s \quad \text{or} \quad \frac{I_p}{I_s} = \frac{n_s}{n_p}$$

If primary and secondary impedances are Z_p and Z_s

$$Z_p = \left(\frac{n_s}{n_p}\right)^2 \times Z_s \quad \text{or} \quad \frac{Z_p}{Z_s} = \left(\frac{n_p}{n_s}\right)^2$$

ie the impedance ratio equals the turns ratio squared and the voltage ratio equals the turns ratio.

Filters

Filters are arrangements of inductors and capacitors which pass frequencies above (and below) a certain frequency and attenuate frequencies below (and above) that frequency.

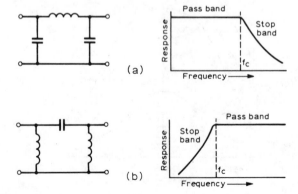

(a)

(b)

These are 'single-section' filters; two or more sections in series can be used to improve their characteristics. Combinations of these basic filters are used to pass a specific band of frequencies ('band pass') or to attenuate a specific band ('band stop').

Filter applications
Filters are used to attenuate unwanted audio or radio frequencies, eg to restrict the AF bandwidth to the minimum required and to attenuate the appropriate radio frequencies in transmitter and TV coaxial antenna feeders.

Mixers
Mixing is the process by which two frequencies are mixed to produce two new frequencies, the sum and the difference of the original frequencies. Small amounts of frequencies harmonically related to the original frequencies may be produced. Unwanted frequencies are removed by subsequent filtering.

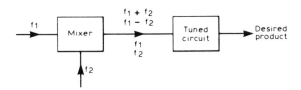

Quartz crystals
The 'piezo-electric effect' is the creation of an electric stress across opposite faces of a thin slice of a crystalline substance (quartz in particular) by a mechanical strain applied. The converse effect also occurs.

A 'crystal' is a slice of quartz which can operate, ie vibrate, at frequencies in the range of about 4kHz to 22MHz according to its dimensions. The slice of quartz is supported by wires attached to electrodes (gold or silver) sputtered on to the crystal face and mounted in an evacuated glass envelope or cold-welded metal container.

The mounted crystal is equivalent to a tuned circuit of very high Q and so may be substituted for the tuned circuit in an oscillator (hence the crystal oscillator). The frequency of a crystal can be altered slightly by variation of the capacitance across it by a varactor diode or a variable capacitor.

Tolerances

A 'tolerance' on the value of a component is a measure of how accurate its indicated value is. Components are generally available with tolerances of $\pm20\%$, $\pm10\%$, $\pm5\%$, $\pm2\%$ and $\pm1\%$. The term is also applied to the accuracy of electrical quantities.

Decibel notation

A method, based on logarithms, of comparing power and voltage at different points in a circuit.

Difference, expressed in decibels (dB), between power W_1 and power W_2 is

$$10 \log_{10} \frac{W_2}{W_1}$$

Since $W = V^2/R$ voltages can also be compared as follows:

$$\frac{W_2}{W_1} = \frac{V_2^{\,2}}{R_2} \div \frac{V_1^{\,2}}{R_1}$$

$$= \frac{V_2^{\,2}}{R_2} \times \frac{R_1}{V_1^{\,2}}$$

If, and only if, $R_1 = R_2$ then

$$\frac{W_2}{W_1} = \frac{V_2^{\,2}}{V_1^{\,2}}$$

hence   No. of decibels $= 10 \log_{10} \dfrac{V_2^{\,2}}{V_1^{\,2}}$

$$= 20 \log_{10} \frac{V_2}{V_1}$$

A magnitude can only be expressed in decibels if a reference level is quoted. 'dBW' is a power level so many decibels above 1W, ie 20dBW is 20dB above 1W, ie 100W. Similarly −20dBW is 20dB down on 1W, ie 10mW.

2. SOLID-STATE DEVICES

These devices are based on 'semiconductors' which are materials whose resistance is between that of a conductor and that of an insulator. The common materials in this category are germanium and silicon. The basic material is produced by the introduction of a very small amount of an impurity into an extremely pure silicon or germanium.

N-type semiconductor material is formed by the addition of phosphorus or arsenic as an impurity. The result appears to be negative as there is a surplus of electrons.

P-type material is formed by introducing aluminium or boron. The result is now positive as there is a 'gap' in each atom which could be filled by an electron. This gap is known as a 'hole'.

PN (junction) diodes

Small pieces of P- type and N-type material formed together result in a 'junction diode'. When the two are connected together, holes move into the N-type and electrons into the P-type. Equilibrium is reached when the region near the junction is devoid of holes and free electrons. This region is the 'depletion layer', typically 0.001mm thick.

The junction may be 'reverse' biased, and a very small amount (the 'leakage current') then flows. If it is 'forward' biased, a large current flows.

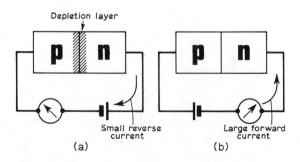

The leakage current is lower and less dependent on temperature in silicon devices than in germanium, and silicon devices are therefore preferred.

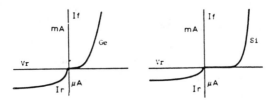

The diode as a rectifier

The silicon diode is used as a rectifier of an alternating voltage in power supplies, but the germanium diode is preferred for RF use (single diode or demodulator).

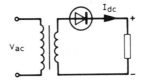

The zener diode

A reverse-biased PN junction in which a very small leakage current flows until the bias is increased up to the 'zener voltage'. Then a sudden increase in current occurs and the voltage across the diode becomes virtually constant.

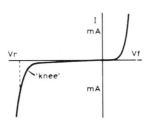

These diodes are used as voltage regulators, providing a direct voltage which is virtually constant. According to type, zener voltage is from 3V to about 150V.

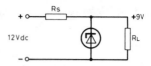

Variable capacitance diodes

Variation of the reverse bias causes the width of the depletion layer to vary, thus the capacitance of the diode varies. This effect can be enhanced in the manufacturing process, creating the 'varactor' diode.

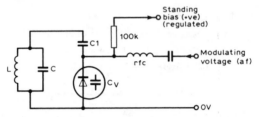

Capacitance ranges of 1–4pF up to 15–150pF are available. These diodes can be used as the variable capacitor in a tuned circuit.

Bipolar transistors

Bipolar transistors consist of three 'pieces' of P-type and N-type material arranged as two junctions back to back.

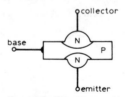

These can be N-P-N as above or P-N-P and may be silicon or germanium, the former being preferred. (Note the difference in the circuit symbols.)

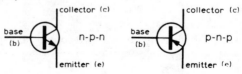

Transistor biasing

The two junctions of a transistor are biased simultaneously.

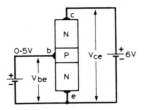

The base-emitter junction is forward biased and the collector-base junction is reverse biased.

The current gain relates change of collector current with change of base current, ie if the collector current changes from 1 to 20mA when the base current changes from 5 to 10μA, current gain (h_{FE}) is 1mA/5μA = 200. Current gain varies from 2 to 800 according to transistor type. 'Transition frequency' (f_T) is the frequency at which current gain has fallen to unity. Transistors are normally used up to 10–15 per cent of f_T.

Characteristics of small-signal (ie input measured in microvolts or millivolts) transistors are typically:

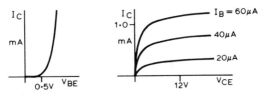

Transistor as small-signal amplifier

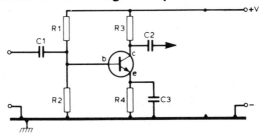

This arrangement is the 'common-emitter' amplifier (the most often used configuration). R1 and R2 provide bias for the base. R3 is the collector load across which the output appears. C1 and C2 provide coupling into and out of the circuit. R4 helps to set up the bias conditions. C3 has very low resistance at the operating frequency, ie to AC it is a virtual short-circuit, and so the emitter appears the same as the 0V line as far as AC is concerned. Base biasing in a transistor amplifier is very critical.

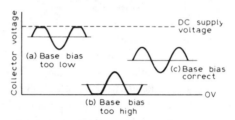

Other transistor configurations

Common-collector (emitter-follower) circuit

The principal feature is that the output resistance is low (of the order of 1000Ω). Thus, although voltage gain is less than 1, it provides a very convenient way of reducing the loading of the following stage upon the previous stage, ie it acts as a buffer between the two stages.

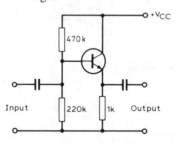

Common-base circuit

In this configuration the input impedance is very low (of the order of 50Ω) but the output impedance is high, and thus very little damping occurs on a tuned circuit used as a collector load. There is also no phase inversion between the input and output voltages as occurs in the other configurations.

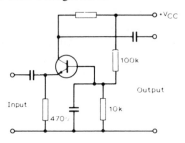

Summary of configurations

Configuration	Input resistance	Output resistance	Current gain
COMMON EMITTER	$(\beta \times r_e) + r_b$ approx 1·4kΩ	Slope of V_c/I_c curve approx 10kΩ to 100kΩ	Varies with types approx 30 to 200
	The common emitter amplifier has the highest power gain of the three configurations		
COMMON BASE	$r_e = \dfrac{26}{I_c} + \dfrac{r_b}{1+h_{fe}}$ approx 13Ω for $I_c = 2$mA	Very high approx 1MΩ or greater	0·98
	The common base amplifier has lower power gain than the common emitter stage but the gain does not fall-off so rapidly at the higher frequencies		
COMMON COLLECTOR (Emitter Follower)	$\beta \times (r_e + R_L) + r_b$ approx 100kΩ for $R_L = 1$kΩ	$r_e = \dfrac{26}{I_c}$ approx 13Ω for $I_c = 2$mA	Same as common emitter approx 30 to 200

Power amplifiers

These are large-signal amplifiers, and supply RF or AF power. The collector load is likely to be, respectively, a tuned circuit or the primary of a transformer. Otherwise the circuit is as the common-emitter amplifier.

Power transistors will have collector currents of 10A or more. The transistor is extremely small, and therefore the power it can dissipate itself is extremely small. Consequently power transistors are mounted on 'heat sinks' in order to increase the effective dissipating area of the device.

The base bias of the common emitter amplifier is set so that both negative and positive half-cycles are amplified equally. This is known as 'Class A' amplification (maximum efficiency is 50%).

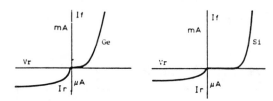

If the base bias is decreased to where conduction ceases, the positive half-cycle is amplified. This is 'Class B' amplification (efficiency 60% to 65%). Further decrease of the bias gives 'Class C' amplification in which less than the positive half-cycle is amplified (efficiency 65% to 70%).

Class B is widely used for AF amplification. Separate transistors for the positive and negative half-cycles are then necessary. This is the 'push-pull' arrangement in which the base and collector currents of each transistor are combined by centre-tapped transformers.

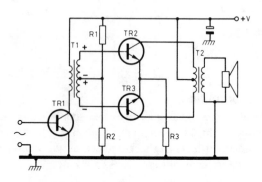

Tuned amplifiers

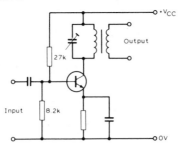

The collector load is a tuned circuit. As the tuned circuit presents significant impedance only at resonance, this circuit gives output only over the frequency band determined by the resonance curve, hence it is known as a 'tuned amplifier', and may be used in all bias conditions: AB, B and C. The collector current has a distorted waveform, but the tuned load results in a much less distorted output waveform.

Frequency multipliers

If the collector load is made to resonate at the second harmonic of the input to a tuned amplifier, due to the distorted collector current waveform, a certain amount of amplification occurs at the second harmonic, and thus frequency doubling occurs. If the collector load resonates at the third harmonic, there will be a reasonable output at the third harmonic ('frequency tripler').

Oscillators

Consider a tuned amplifier in which a small amount of the output is inductively coupled back to the input (base) of the amplifier. The phase of the signal fed back may be negative, so that it is subtracted from the input signal. Alternatively it may be positive and added to the input signal. In this case the output is increased and more is fed back to the input. The situation then arises that the input to the amplifier may be removed and the circuit continues to function on the voltage fed back from output to input. Thus the circuit is oscillating and is known as an 'oscillator'.

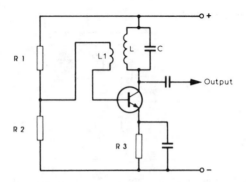

Provided that feedback is positive (in this example the phase of the feedback is determined by the way round that L1 is connected) and that the feedback voltage is adequate to overcome the circuit losses, any amplifier will oscillate.

Though there are many forms of oscillator, they only differ in the way that the feedback is arranged. Most common are the Colpitts and Clapp-Gouriet circuit.

Use of the transistor as a switch

The basis of digital circuits is the state of a switch which is either ON (1) or OFF (0). This requirement is very simply met by a transistor which is either conducting or not conducting.

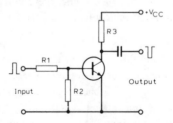

R1 limits the base current, and R2 keeps the transistor non-conducting (Class C) or OFF with no input present. If input rises, the transistor conducts, ie switches ON, and a voltage drop occurs across R3. Note that R3 could be replaced by a relay or a lamp.

Field-effect transistors

The N-type FET consists essentially of a P-type region, the 'gate' (g), diffused into an N-type channel, the ends of which are the 'source' (s) and the 'drain' (d). The main current flow is from drain to source. This current is controlled by the voltage applied to the gate (ie the FET is a voltage-controlled device).

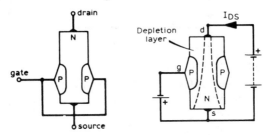

By varying the voltage (negative) on the gate, the width of the depletion layer is varied. Ultimately the drain current is reduced to zero ('pinched off').

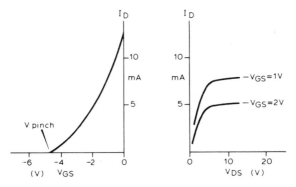

The channel could be made of P-type material, in which case the potentials would be reversed.

The FET is another form of transistor which can be used in all the applications discussed. It has the great advantage of very high input impedance and exists in many forms, eg the IGFET and dual-gate MOSFET which is particularly useful as a mixer.

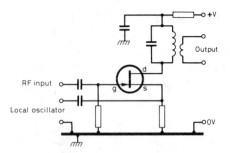

Integrated circuits

Integrated circuits (ICs) result from the extension of transistor fabrication techniques to the formation of complete circuits of transistors, diodes, resistors, capacitors and inductors (both of limited value) on to a single, small N- or P-type silicon substrate (the 'chip').

Thus circuits of all types, RF, IF and AF amplifiers, modulators, demodulators etc can be fabricated. Most basic low-power stages used in transmitters and receivers can now be produced with few peripheral components. Equipment is therefore becoming more complex, smaller and more reliable.

3. TRANSMITTERS

Requirements

The amateur transmitter must:

(a) produce output power desired;

(b) not drift in frequency;

(c) probably operate on several frequency bands;

(d) have pure output waveform, ie no harmonics or parasitic oscillations.

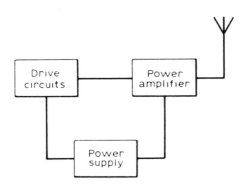

'Drive circuits' generate the RF input to the power amplifier, and may include modulation circuits.

The 'power amplifier' (PA) provides the power output required.

The 'power supply' provides the supplies required.

It must be possible to set the transmitter frequency to any particular value in a given band, and hence the VFO is the basic RF source for the drive circuits.

Transmitter drive circuits

Transmitter drive circuits may consist of:

(a) frequency multiplier chain;

(b) mixer-VFO;

(c) frequency synthesiser.

Frequency multiplier chain

1. Convenient for a number of bands in harmonic relationship, eg the original HF bands 1.8–28MHz, but frequency drift in the VFO is also multiplied.
2. Multiplication of a 6MHz or 8MHz source to 144MHz or 430MHz bands.

Radiation of harmonics other than the desired one, which could cause interference to other services, must be prevented by screening and filtering etc.

Mixer-VFO

A mixer combines the outputs of a VFO (typical coverage of 500kHz in range of 3–8MHz) and a crystal oscillator. With the appropriate crystal frequency, output at almost any frequency may be obtained.

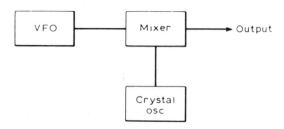

Any frequency drift in a VFO is the same at all output frequencies as it is added and not multiplied.

Frequency synthesisers

These are complex circuits which produce a number of equally spaced frequencies, the stability of which is determined by a single crystal.

They can replace the oscillator as the controlling frequency source in the transmitter and/or receiver in communication systems based on equally spaced channels.

The basis is a 'phase-locked loop', ie a feedback loop which compares the frequency of a voltage-controlled oscillator with that of a crystal-controlled reference oscillator (1–5MHz). The VCO is an oscillator frequency whose frequency can be varied by means of a varactor. The frequencies of the reference oscillator and the VCO are compared by a phase detector which generates an error voltage which is fed to the varactor. The reference and VCO frequencies do not necessarily have to be the same. The feedback loop can include a counter (divider) circuit so that the VCO operates at n times the reference frequency as below.

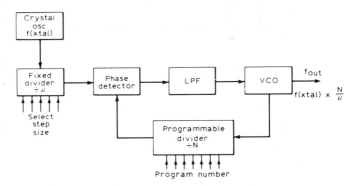

In the case of the HF receiver the 'step size', which is the channel spacing at VHF, must not be greater than 100Hz and preferably less for satisfactory tuning. Also it should be switchable to 1kHz or 10kHz for rapid tuning. Programming to achieve this can be complicated and depends on complexity/cost of the equipment. Actual frequency is shown on a digital display.

Variable frequency oscillators

Frequency stability is of prime importance because transmission must not drift out of:

(a) the band in use;
(b) the pass band of a receiver tuned to the transmission. Frequency drift may also cause interference with other signals.

Common circuits are the Colpitts and the Clapp-Gouriet.

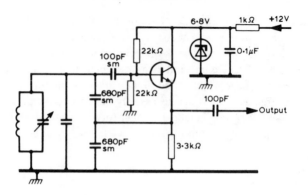

Factors governing stability

1. Mechanical stability of a tuned circuit:

   (a) coil wound under tension on grooved ceramic former;

   (b) mechanically sound, good-quality variable capacitor;

   (c) short rigid wiring between coil and variable capacitor (also applies to all oscillator wiring);

   (d) tuned circuit mounted away from any heat source since heat will cause the coil and capacitor to move.

2. Any other capacitors associated with the tuned circuit (ie feedback capacitors in Colpitts and similar circuits which swamp out any change in transistor capacitance) should be good-quality mica types. The positive temperature coefficient of these may be compensated by a negative-temperature coefficient ceramic capacitor.

3. The loading of the next stage on the VFO should be as light as possible. Ideally, follow the VFO by a Class A amplifier or emitter follower.

4. Operate the VFO from regulated voltage.

5. Do not key the VFO.

6. Operate the VFO at the lowest frequency possible.

Frequency multipliers

Frequency multipliers normally operate in Class C to produce more harmonics – the required one, usually second or third, is selected by the tuned circuit, which may be:

(a) a normal variable capacitor and small coil;
(b) a fixed capacitor (possibly 'strays') and slug-tuned coil.

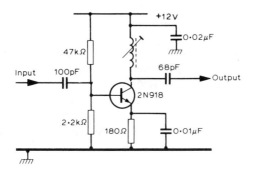

Buffer amplifiers

A buffer amplifier (BA) may be used to isolate the VFO or to increase drive to the PA, and can be tuned or untuned. The collector load in an untuned BA may be an RF choke or a low-value resistor. An untuned BA is not very effective above 2MHz and so is generally used after a VFO. In the tuned BA, a tuned circuit resonates at the input frequency, and hence, to avoid oscillation, input generally needs to be screened from the output (circuit as above).

Power amplifiers at HF

High-power transistors have very low input and output imped-ances (in the order of 1–10Ω). Therefore, nominal 50Ω RF input to a transistor is stepped down to about 5Ω and the output impedance of the transistor is stepped up to the normal 50Ω as shown overleaf.

c

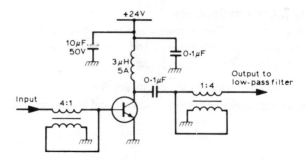

Input and output transformers are 'broad-band', 3–30MHz. Thus no tuning is required but any unwanted harmonic or spurious frequency is also amplified. Consequently, filters between the output stage and the antenna are required.

Design and layout are critical; adequate heat sinking must be used. Bypassing of the collector supply is critical to prevent instability (spurious oscillation).

Power amplifiers at VHF

Due to the more effective antennas available for VHF, low-power operation is common as the transistor is a cheap and convenient solution for powers up to about 25W.

A typical arrangement is:

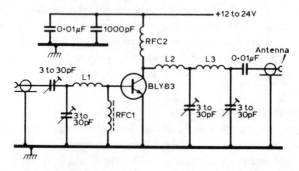

This uses the L-pi output circuit and gives an output of 7W at 12V supply and 12W at 24V.

Modulation

The output of a transmitter is an alternating waveform of desired amplitude (depends on power level and output impedance – generally 50–75Ω) and frequency. It should be a pure sine wave, ie with no harmonics to cause interference to other services. It is known as the 'carrier wave'.

To convey information, the carrier wave can be switched on and off (keyed) to form morse code; known as 'CW telegraphy' or just 'CW'.

Some characteristics of the carrier wave can be varied in sympathy with the message. This process is called 'modulation'. Each mode of modulation requires a particular form of demodulation in the receiver.

Amplitude modulation (AM):
Amplitude of the RF carrier is varied at audio frequency (AF).

Frequency modulation (FM):
Frequency of the RF carrier is varied at AF.

Sidebands:
Additional frequencies above and below carrier frequency which are created in any modulation system.

Bandwidth:
Total width of sidebands produced in AM is twice the highest audio frequency.

Bandwidth required

Intelligible transmission of speech requires that frequencies up to about 2.5kHz need be transmitted. Thus bandwidth is 5kHz with AM.

Single sideband operation (SSB)

In AM each sideband contains the same information and the carrier contains no information, so the carrier and one or the other sideband can be suppressed.

Deviation

'Deviation' is the change in the frequency of the carrier wave in an FM system. Total change (+ and −) is the 'swing', ie 2 × deviation.

Narrow-band frequency modulation (NBFM)

This is FM in which the deviation is restricted to 2.5kHz, ie the same bandwidth as required by communication-quality AM.

Modulation depth

'Modulation depth' is the amount of amplitude modulation applied. Maximum is 100% or modulation factor of 1. At 100% modulation, the negative peak of the modulating waveform reduces the carrier amplitude to zero and the positive peak increases carrier amplitude to twice the unmodulated value.

Over-modulation (AM)

Excessive modulating voltage causes negative peak to break up the carrier, creating spurious sidebands and considerable interference.

Over-modulation (FM)

This is known as 'over-deviation'. An increase in amplitude of the modulating signal causes a corresponding increase in deviation of the transmitter. The recommended deviation may be exceeded and the transmission will occupy a wider bandwidth than necessary.

Modulation methods

Amplitude modulation

The effective power in a carrier wave modulated to a depth of a 100% by a sinusoidal modulating signal is 1.5 times the unmodulated carrier power.

This extra power is supplied by the modulator (audio amplifier). This is coupled into the HT supply to the PA stage by the modulation transformer which transforms the output impedance of the modulator to the modulating impedance of the PA.

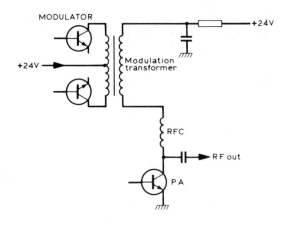

Frequency modulation

Direct frequency modulation may be achieved by varying the frequency of the fundamental oscillator, eg by a varactor diode acting on the tuned circuit of the oscillator. In a multiplier-type exciter, the deviation of the fundamental oscillator is also multiplied. A crystal oscillator, driving multipliers to 144MHz, can be deviated by the small amount required (200Hz or so) by a varactor.

Single sideband

Requirements are:

(a) suppression of carrier wave as it contains no information;

(b) elimination of one sideband as both contain the same information.

The basis of sideband generation is a 'balanced modulator', a form of bridge circuit into which the carrier frequency (RF) and the modulating frequency (AF) are fed. When correctly balanced, the carrier is suppressed, leaving only the sidebands, one of which is removed by a filter.

Filter characteristics are critical. The bandwidth should be about 2.5kHz and 'shape factor' (ratio of bandwidth at −60dB and −6dB) should be 1.5–2.

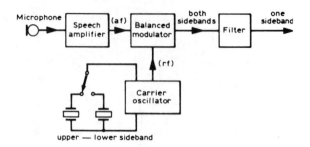

Sideband is usually generated in the megahertz region (typically 9MHz) in which case a sideband would be 9.000–9.003MHz. Frequency conversion to the desired bands must be by mixing.

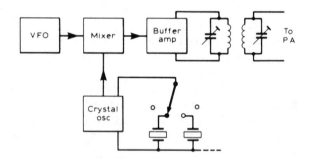

A combination of the previous two diagrams gives a block diagram of an SSB transmitter (sideband generation at 9MHz).

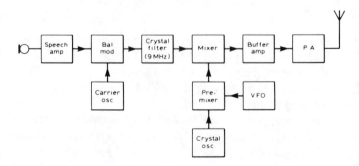

PA is a linear amplifier to amplify a modulated RF signal without distortion. Upper sideband is normally transmitted above 10MHz and lower sideband below 10MHz.

Keying

Switching a transmitter on and off to form the dots and dashes of the morse code can create serious interference. It should be done at a point where the current is minimal. A VFO should not be keyed; VFO supply should be regulated.

Transmitter power level

Maximum *output* power permitted on most bands by the UK licence is now 26dBW which is equivalent to 400W. In the case of SSB this is the peak envelope power (PEP).

Speech processing

Speech has a very peaky waveform, and hence the maximum amplitude can be very high, but the average amplitude is quite low. The object of a speech processor is to amplify this waveform but to limit the infrequent peaks. The average level of the waveform is therefore increased. If this process is carried too far, noticeable distortion is introduced.

Transmitter adjustment

All tuning and adjustment of a transmitter must be done on a dummy load. The critical adjustment, irrespective of the modulation system in use, is that of the modulation level. If this is set too high, considerable interference and distortion are caused, particularly when SSB is used.

Transmitter interference

A transmitter, particularly at high power, is a potential source of interference to television and other services. The implications of this are discussed in Sections 7 and 8.

Comparison of modes of modulation

SSB

1. Only one sideband is transmitted, hence makes most use of the RF spectrum.
2. There are no beats between adjacent carrier waves.
3. Less affected by disturbances in propagation.

NBFM

1. Good solid coverage of relatively small area which can be increased by repeaters and exceptional propagation conditions.
2. Widely used due to availability of small and relatively cheap equipment for mobile and hand-held use.
3. No variation of amplitude of carrier, hence less chance of interference.

Symbols for common modes

Telegraphy	A1A
Telephony (AM)	A3E
Telephony (FM)	F3E
Telephony (SSB)	J3E

The use of valves in linear amplifiers

(Note: this subject will not be examined before 1994.)

Linear amplifiers are generally used in the grounded-grid circuit shown in which the grid of the valve is earthed and the RF drive from the transceiver is applied to the cathode, which may be indirectly or directly heated. A directly heated cathode, ie the 'filament', must be isolated for RF from ground. This is achieved by supplying the filament power via a bifilar choke wound on a ferrite rod.

If the valve has an indirectly heated cathode, there is generally sufficient isolation between the cathode and ground.

The RF drive required is high but is within the capability of most transceivers. A proportion of this drive is fed through the valve and appears at the anode. Neutralisation is not required if the valve is a triode, and stability is improved.

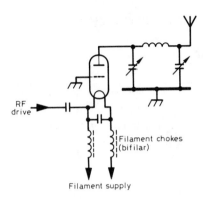

Filament supply

Valves used are low-power to medium-power transmitting types, two to four being connected in parallel. Examples, with their approximate PEP output, are one or two 3-500Z (1–2kW), three or four 811A (600–800W), two 572B (800–1000W) and two 813 (1kW). A power supply of up to 2200V is required, and this would be obtained from a bridge rectifier circuit with a series/parallel bank of electrolytic capacitors for smoothing.

An alternative circuit uses up to four colour-TV line-output valves (indirectly heated tetrodes) in parallel. This arrangement is capable of an output of 400–600W with an anode supply of 800–900V. These valves are normally used as triodes by connecting the screen grid to the control grid.

The circuits of linear amplifiers are relatively simple but use large components. For this reason they are often home built.

At VHF and UHF the 4CX250B valve would be used.

4. RECEIVERS

Receiver characteristics

Sensitivity

The ability to receive weak signals. Normally quoted as the signal input necessary to produce at the output a standard ratio of signal to background noise. For example, a good receiver would need a signal input of less than 0.5V to produce a signal-to-noise ratio of 20dB at the output.

Selectivity

The ability to receive one signal and disregard another on a nearby frequency. High selectivity is necessary in an amateur band receiver.

A good receiver would have a response which is 6dB down 2.5kHz away from the wanted signal and 60dB down 5kHz from the wanted signal. Even higher selectivity is required for the satisfactory reception of telegraphy signals.

Bandwidth

The above receiver has a bandwidth of 2.5kHz at 6dB down and so on.

Frequency stability

The ability to remain tuned to the desired signal. An unstable receiver is said to 'drift' in frequency.

Stability is determined by the design and construction of the oscillator stage which should be made with the same care as the transmitter VFO.

Dynamic range

The difference in level between the maximum signal a receiver will accept, and the minimum signal which will give a usable output. Quoted in decibels – in a good receiver it would be in the order of 100dB.

AGC (automatic gain control)

The automatic control of gain and hence sensitivity by the strength of the received signal. If the signal is weak, the gain is increased and vice versa. Therefore the output is reasonably constant as the signal fades.

The superhet receiver

In the superhet receiver all incoming signals are converted to a fairly low frequency, the intermediate frequency (IF), at which most of the receiver's gain and selectivity is obtained. The IF amplifier is followed by a detector (demodulator) for each mode. The detector is followed by an audio amplifier.

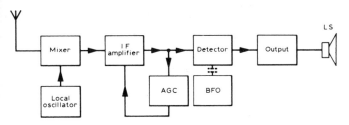

The output of an oscillator operating at the IF is coupled to the demodulator to facilitate reception of CW or SSB. AGC is applied to the IF amplifier.

Mixer

The mixing process in the superhet is shown below.

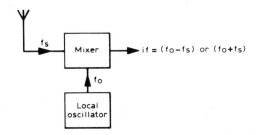

The mixer is followed by the IF amplifier, ie an amplifier which is tuned to the IF. The unwanted output of the mixer is therefore rejected.

It is possible that two input signals can result in the same IF as shown below.

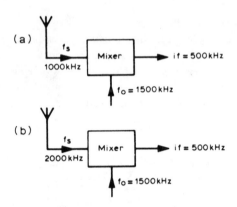

(a) is the situation which is required, but if there is a strong signal on a frequency which is twice the IF away from the wanted signal, ie situation (b), the receiver receives both signals.

This is 'image' interference, and is a spurious response of the receiver. A fairly common example is the reception of a powerful 19m broadcast station in parts of the 20m amateur band on a simple all-wave receiver which has the standard IF of about 455kHz. This type of interference may be reduced by increasing the IF or by using one or two stages of amplification before the mixer.

Local oscillator

The mixer and its associated oscillator are generally separate stages. The stability requirements of a transmitter VFO apply equally to the receiver local oscillator (LO) which generally operates on the high side of the signal frequency. A typical mixer oscillator is shown opposite.

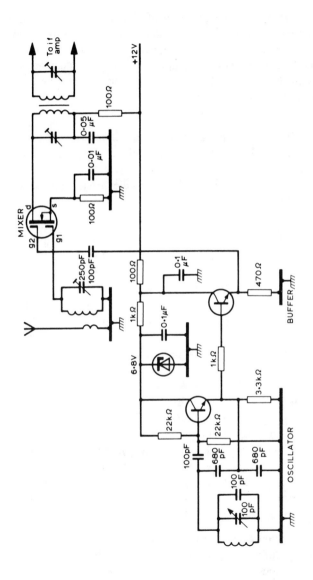

'Tracking' is the requirement of the LO to maintain throughout its range a constant frequency difference from that of the mixer tuned circuit. The aim is to achieve correct tracking at ends and middle of each range by adjustment of coil inductance and a trimmer across the LO tuning capacitor. Alternatively, a frequency synthesiser may be used.

RF amplifiers

Amplification at the signal frequency will increase the signal-to-noise ratio. The extra selectivity will reduce the possibility of image interference and will reduce radiation from the local oscillator via the antenna. However, the provision of RF stages depends upon the overall gain of the receiver.

IF amplifiers

Probably the most important section of a receiver, as most of the gain and selectivity are created here. The bandwidth required is typically 2.5kHz (for SSB) and 250Hz (for CW).

Selectivity can be achieved in several ways:

1. A number of paired coupled tuned circuits. Such a pair of preset tuned circuits in a screening can is an 'IF transformer'. Variation of the coupling factor, either mechanically or electrically, presents a difficult design problem, and hence often a single bandwidth is provided. This not a good solution as many wish to use both SSB and CW.
2. The double superhet with two IFs, the first around 1.6MHz and the second around 100kHz. The first IF which is followed by a second mixer ensures an improved second-channel performance and the second (low-frequency) section of the IF amplifier with two stages will provide a bandwidth of 1.5–2kHz.
3. A preferred arrangement is an IF amplifier using a crystal or mechanical band-pass filter. These are made for various frequencies and bandwidths.

The demodulator (detector)

This 'rectifies' or 'demodulates' the output of the IF amplifier; the modulation which was superimposed on the transmitter carrier can be recovered as a varying direct voltage. For optimum performance each modulation method requires a particular demodulator.

Diode or envelope detector

This form of detector operates as a half-wave rectifier (cf 'Power supplies'), and its output is developed across a resistor (diode load). It is often called an 'envelope detector' as it recovers the amplitude modulation envelope and is satisfactory for CW when used with a BFO to provide an audible beat note. Detection of an SSB signal requires the insertion of a signal into the detector to simulate the carrier which was suppressed in the transmitter. A BFO can fulfil this function but it is not the optimum arrangement.

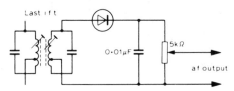

Product detector

This is the preferred arrangement for SSB (also satisfactory for CW). It is a mixer circuit which combines the IF signal with the output of the carrier insertion oscillator (CIO) which is generally crystal controlled. A typical circuit is:

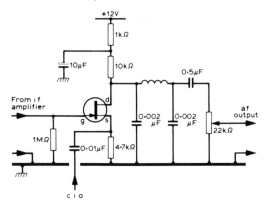

Ratio detector

This, the most common FM demodulator, is not sensitive to amplitude variation of the IF signal. At the centre frequency voltages applied to the diodes are equal. As the frequency varies, so does the voltage applied to the diodes and hence the rectified voltages across C1 and C2. The output at C is proportional to the ratio of voltages across C1 and C2. The total voltage is held constant by C3.

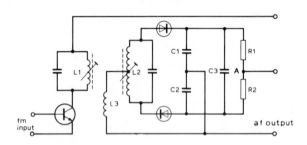

This type of demodulator is now being superseded by an integrated-circuit version.

Automatic gain control

The output of the IF amplifier is rectified in the diode circuit to produce a voltage which is used as a bias voltage to control the gain of the IF amplifier. Similarly the gain is increased when a weak signal is received. AGC largely cancels the effect of signal fades and so the output of the receiver is reasonably constant. AGC is generally switched out of operation for the reception of CW signals.

In the basic circuit the AGC voltage is obtained from the detector diode. A separate diode for AGC purposes is often used. Other refinements appear in the more expensive receivers; these may include amplification of the AGC to provide greater range of control and switching of operating time of the AGC system according to the type of signal received.

Audio amplifier

A conventional audio amplifier, output 1–2W, to a small internal speaker. Generally there is provision for the use of headphones.

Some receivers, particularly the older type, incorporate some additional selectivity in the audio circuits, often a very sharp peak of amplification at about 1000Hz with a bandwidth of 100Hz.

Noise limiters and blankers

The object is to reduce to an acceptable level the interference created every time a spark occurs. The limiter is an arrangement of diodes which 'clip', ie limit, the amplitude of the pulses of interference at the level of the modulation on the signal.

The blanker is a complex circuit in which the interfering pulses are selected, amplified and demodulated. The resulting waveform is fed back into the receiver and 'blanks' out the interference before it reaches the receiver output.

Squelch circuits

The object is to switch off the audio output of an FM receiver in the absence of a signal, thus eliminating the annoying hiss produced by the receiver. The level at which squelch comes into operation is normally adjustable.

The transceiver

The frequency stability of the transmitter and receiver in an SSB system is critical. The carrier insertion must also be done accurately.

A filter (bandwidth 2.5kHz and shape factor 1.5–2) is required in the transmitter and receiver. This, combined with the necessity for a highly stable oscillator in each, has resulted in the development of the 'transceiver' in which the same VFO and filter operate in both functions. This is now the preferred equipment for amateur SSB and CW on all bands.

Nominal output of most transceivers is 100W. For higher power they are followed by a separate linear amplifier in which there is a linear relationship between output and input, ie there is no distortion.

D

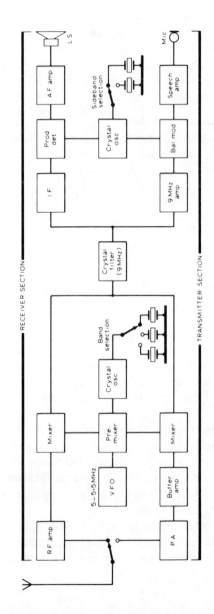

The transverter

This enables an HF band transceiver to be used on other bands
(generally 144MHz or 432MHz).

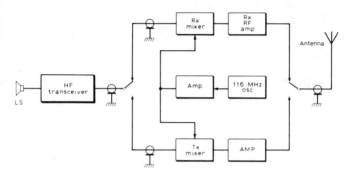

Its function is to combine the transmit frequency conversion
(generally upwards) and the receive frequency conversion (generally downwards) using a common crystal-controlled oscillator.

5. POWER SUPPLIES

Direct supplies of up to 12V for mobile and hand-held equipment may be obtained from batteries of primary or secondary cells. Fixed equipment is normally served by a power unit which transforms, rectifies and smooths the 240V 50Hz mains supply. The maximum requirement is usually 13.5V at a current peaking at 30–40A.

Rectifying circuits
Silicon power diodes are used as the rectifying element.

Half-wave circuit

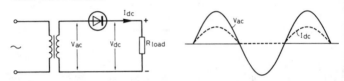

Note the voltage and current waveforms; and that if the diode is reversed, it is the negative half-cycle which is rectified.

Full-wave circuit

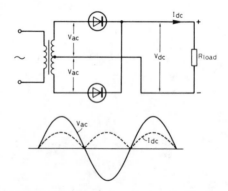

This is a combination of two half-wave circuits. Note the variation in amplitude of the current waveform. This is the 'ripple' which is the variation in amplitude of the rectified waveform. It is a 'direct' voltage as it varies between zero and a positive maximum. Ripple frequency is 100Hz.

Bridge circuit

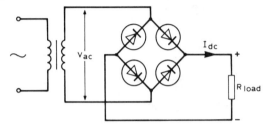

Note that a centre-tapped secondary winding is not required. Ripple frequency is 100Hz.

Smoothing circuits

A high-value capacitor may be connected across the rectifier/load. This is the 'reservoir' capacitor.

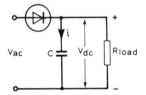

It charges up to the peak value of V_{ac} and so stores energy during the positive half-cycle and supplies it to the load during the negative half-cycle as follows:

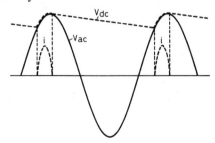

The fluctuations in V_{ac}, ie the amplitude of the ripple, are therefore very much reduced or 'smoothed'.

Further smoothing could be achieved by the addition of another capacitor and a 'smoothing' choke.

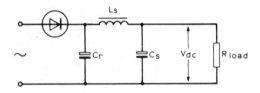

However, most power supplies of this type are high-current supplies in which case smoothing must be by very high capacitance, eg up to 68,000μF.

Diode protection

Rectifier diodes have a very low forward impedance and so can deal with large currents, and thus a sharp increase in voltage (switching surge) may cause a large surge current which could destroy the diode. This can be prevented by a capacitor across the diode and a resistor in series with it. Such a capacitor reduces the amplitude of the switching transients when the diode turns off rapidly under reverse bias conditions. A single diode is normally adequate as a rectifying element in 12V supplies. Should it be necessary to use two or more in series, a resistor should be connected across each to equalise the voltage drop across each.

Power supply characteristics

'Regulation' is the change in output voltage of a power unit between no load and full load. It is important if the load current varies between wide limits.

Bad regulation is caused by excessive voltage drop within the power unit itself, generally the result of inadequate design. Thus an ideal power supply has a low 'source impedance'. Some circuits may require a supply having a very low ripple voltage.

A roughly stabilised (or regulated) supply is generally suitable
for a VFO. This can be obtained by the appropriate zener diode (up
to 150V may be obtained in this way). However, the above criteria
are adequately met by an electronically stabilised supply.

Stabilised power supplies

Basis is the use of a transistor, the series or pass transistor (TR1),
in series with the supply to the load.

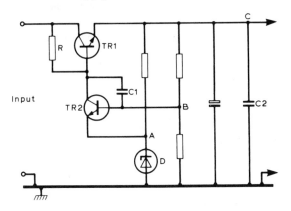

The zener diode provides a reference voltage which holds the
base of the pass transistor fairly constant. As the load current
increases, the voltage at the emitter tends to fall and so the
transistor conducts more easily and so maintains the output
voltage constant.

This type of supply would be used to provide 13.5V at 35–40A
to a transceiver. Its design is critical; the 'pass transistor' would be
two or more devices in parallel and adequate protective circuits
would be built in to switch off the supply quickly if there was a
fault which would cause the output voltage to rise to the detriment
of the transceiver output transistors.

Smaller supplies are based on the integrated circuit regulator
containing the series element, reference supply, error amplifier
and sensing resistors.

6. PROPAGATION AND ANTENNAS

Propagation

Radio communication depends upon the radiation of electromagnetic waves from the transmitting antenna. These waves are created by the RF currents in the antenna which arise from the coupling of the transmitter output into the antenna.

Radiation can be considered as a succession of concentric spheres of electric force moving outwards at constant speed. This is the 'electric field'. At right-angles to and inseparable from the electric field is the 'magnetic field' made up of magnetic lines of force.

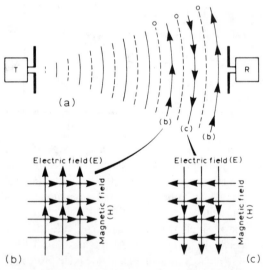

The velocity of propagation (c) of electromagnetic waves in space is approximately 300×10^6 metres per second.

$$c = f \times \lambda$$

where λ = wavelength (distance travelled to complete one cycle)
and f = frequency

hence
$$\lambda = \frac{300,000,000}{f(\text{Hz})} = \frac{300}{f(\text{MHz})}$$

Polarisation of electromagnetic waves

Waves are said to be 'polarised' in the direction of (ie parallel to) the electric lines of force. Polarisation is usually parallel to the length of the antenna but occasionally can be modified by atmospheric conditions.

Field strength at the receiving antenna may range from less than $1\mu\text{V/m}$ to more than 100mV/m.

Modes of propagation

1. Ground or (surface) wave
2. Ionospheric wave (sky wave)
3. Tropospheric

Ground wave propagation

This is the main mode of propagation up to 1–2MHz. Attenuation increases rapidly above 2MHz. Ground wave is not so affected by atmospheric effects etc as other modes, particularly below about 0.5MHz.

Ionospheric propagation

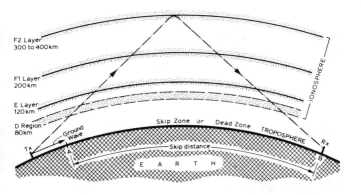

Caused by refraction in ionised layers (E, F1 and F2) above the earth's surface. It is the major mode of propagation within the 1–30MHz band. These layers are the result of radiation from the sun and so intensity of radiation varies over the day and the year, with a slow variation over the 11-year sunspot cycle. Consequently, there is considerable variation in propagation by this mode.

Critical frequency
This is the highest frequency reflected when radiation is vertical. At maximum about noon each day.

Maximum usable frequency (MUF)
This is the highest frequency which can be reflected over a given distance. It depends upon many factors: season, time of day, latitude, state of sunspot cycle, angle of radiation etc.

Around sunspot maximum, MUF may exceed 50MHz, but at minimum it does not often exceed 25MHz.

Note that:

(a) peak value of MUF occurs between 1000 and 1600 hours;
(b) peak values are higher at sunspot maximum;
(c) peak values are higher in winter than in summer;
(d) there is much higher variation of MUF over the day in winter than in summer;
(e) generally, the MUF is higher in a north-south direction than in an east-west direction.

Sporadic E propagation
Random patches of intense ionisation in the E layer (often in summer) cause reflection of frequencies up to 100MHz or so, and sometimes up to 150MHz, which may last from an hour or less to several days.

D region
Less clearly defined than a layer, its major significance is that under abnormal circumstances, it can absorb the frequencies under discussion.

Skip (or dead) zone
A region in which signals are not reflected from the layers. Note also skip distance.

Sudden ionospheric disturbance (SID)
Solar flares increase ultraviolet and X-radiation from the sun which greatly increases ionisation in the D region. Hence radio waves are absorbed before they reach the reflecting layers. The result is complete interruption of communication for a few minutes to an hour or so (Dellinger fade-out).

Ionospheric storm
This often occurs two days after an SID. It is thought to be caused by slower-moving particles emitted at the same time as the solar flare, which increases ionisation in the D region and decreases it in the F layer. The resulting fade-out may last for several days.

Fading of a signal
The strength of a signal received at a given point is rarely constant because of continually changing conditions in the ionosphere, layer height, ionisation level, skip distance etc. The signal may also arrive by two different paths, ie one and/or two reflections.

Effects are minimised by AGC in the receiver.

Tropospheric propagation
This is the major mode of propagation beyond line-of-sight at frequencies above about 50MHz.

Changes in temperature, pressure and humidity (ie weather) cause variations in the refractive index of the lower atmosphere (up to 17km).

These variations affect the propagation:

(a) localised variations cause scattering of radio waves (tropo-scatter, used commercially);
(b) sharp changes between horizontal layers cause reflection of radio waves;
(c) a sharp decrease in refractive index with height creates ducts.

Ducting

A 'duct' is a region of indeterminate shape, but possibly only 50m high, which can propagate radio waves with extremely low attenuation over long distances. Waves may leak out at any point. It is not a reliable mode of propagation.

Mode of propagation depends on frequency, but no sharp transition. At some frequencies, significant propagation may occur by more than one mode.

Propagation at VHF can also occur by scattering or random reflection from auroral zones round the poles, and meteor trails.

Antennas

A fundamental antenna is a piece of wire, one half-wavelength long, in free space (remote from all objects). Voltage and current vary along this antenna as shown:

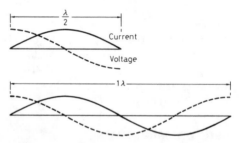

The variations over a full-wave antenna operating at its second harmonic are as in the lower diagram.

Resonant antenna

This is an antenna which exhibits a standing-wave pattern as shown above. It is an efficient radiator and has similar properties to a tuned circuit. Length is related to the frequency (wavelength) of operation.

Impedance of an antenna

The ratio of voltage and current along an antenna varies widely, and may be resistive, capacitive or inductive.

Radiation resistance

The resistance which would dissipate the power which the antenna radiates.

Length of an antenna

The physical (actual) length of an antenna is somewhat less than the electrical length due to:

(a) velocity of propagation being less in a wire than in free space;

(b) presence of buildings etc;

(c) finite diameter of wire or element.

Physical length is taken to be 0.95 of the electrical length. This constant is the correction factor (k).

Hence half-wavelength $= \dfrac{150 \times 0.95}{f(\text{MHz})} = \dfrac{143}{f(\text{MHz})}$ metres

Radiation patterns

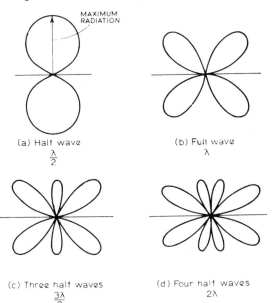

(a) Half wave
$\dfrac{\lambda}{2}$

(b) Full wave
λ

(c) Three half waves
$\dfrac{3\lambda}{2}$

(d) Four half waves
2λ

The diagram shows the direction in which a horizontal antenna will radiate (in free space). Patterns are three-dimensional.

In practice, these patterns will be modified by the presence of buildings, trees etc, and the nearness of the earth. If one end is tilted, lobes move together. Consideration of the $\lambda/2$ pattern shows that for a vertical antenna, radiation is omni-directional.

Angle of radiation
The angle with respect to the horizon at which most radiation occurs. It depends mainly upon the height of the antenna (preferably at least $\lambda/2$). For long-distance communication, a low angle of radiation is necessary.

Directional (beam) antenna
An antenna in which radiation pattern is modified to concentrate the radiation in a particular direction. It is commonly achieved by the addition of a director and reflector (parasitic elements) to a half-wave antenna, as shown with the resulting radiation pattern. This is the Yagi antenna (basis of the three-element beam).

Coupling transmitter to antenna
Antennas should be as high as possible and as far as possible from buildings etc. Power must therefore be transferred from the transmitter to the antenna by means of a feeder, commonly a:

(a) coaxial cable (unbalanced) 50Ω and 70Ω;
(b) twin feeder (balanced) 75Ω and 300Ω;
(c) single-wire feeder.

If the transmission line is not matched, power is reflected from the antenna (load) to the transmitter (source). Voltage and current vary along the line. Standing wave ratio (SWR) is the measure of this and hence of the effectiveness of the antenna system. A perfect system will have SWR of 1.0 to 1. Solid-state transmitters will switch off or reduce power if SWR exceeds about 2.5 to 1.

Antenna tuning unit (ATU)
This 'matches', not tunes the antenna. It is basically a tuned circuit resonant at the transmitter frequency.

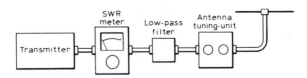

The transmission line (50Ω or 70Ω coaxial cable) is usually short. The low-pass filter design impedance would be 50–70Ω.

Typical antennas

1. Dipole

The centre impedance of a half-wave antenna is about 75Ω, therefore it can be fed at this point with 75Ω coaxial cable. Centre impedance at the third harmonic is only slightly higher (90Ω) so that an acceptable match exists, but at all other frequencies a severe mismatch occurs. The only practical application of this property is a 7MHz dipole which operates satisfactorily at 21MHz.

The dipole is often fed with coaxial cable. Note that input to the dipole is balanced and coaxial cable is unbalanced. The preferred arrangement is the use of a 'balance-unbalance transformer' (balun) between the dipole and the coaxial feeder (an alternative is to feed the antenna with twin-feeder and have the balun at the transmitter output).

The dipole is a commonly used, very effective antenna. Apart from the 7MHz/21MHz case, it is a single-band antenna.

2. Trap dipole

This is a dipole containing, at a particular point, a 'trap' or parallel-tuned circuit. At resonance, the trap is of high impedance and so isolates the following portion. The standard arrangement is shown below.

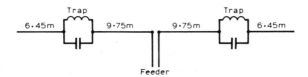

The traps are resonant at 7MHz and isolate the end sections, and therefore it is a normal dipole at this frequency. At 3.5MHz, inductance of the traps lengthens the end sections, making this equivalent to a 3.5MHz dipole. At 14MHz, 21MHz and 28MHz, the traps provide series capacitance, effectively shortening the top to resonate at odd harmonics and so function as a $3\lambda/2$, $5\lambda/2$ and $7\lambda/2$ antenna respectively.

The trap dipole, though a compromise, operates fairly satisfactorily on these five bands.

3. Three-element beam

This is a common, commercially available, directional antenna for the 14, 21 and 28MHz bands. It consists of a radiator, a reflector and a director, all of which are trapped for multiband operation. The addition of a reflector and a director reduces the centre impedance to the order of 20Ω, so that in a single-band beam some form of impedance matching is required to match to normal coaxial cable. In the trapped three-band beam, the fixed spacing between the elements results in an acceptable match to 50Ω cable on the three bands.

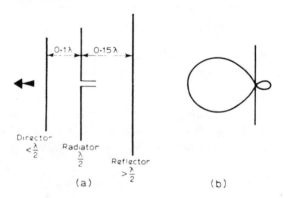

4. Quad antenna

The basic quad is a square loop of wire normally fed at the bottom (impedance 75Ω), and the length of each side is $\lambda/4$. Parasitic elements can be added, and the most popular version of this antenna is the nest of three two-element quads (radiator and reflector) for 14MHz, 21MHz and 28MHz.

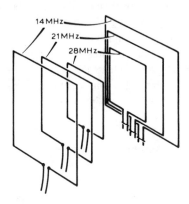

Published data suggest that the quad has a slightly better forward gain and noticeably better front-to-back ratio than the Yagi.

5. End-fed antennas

A random length of wire, preferably resonant, ie 33, 66 or 132ft, brought straight to the transmitter antenna socket.

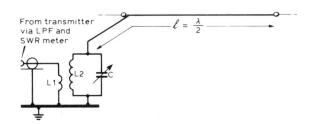

This is a convenient antenna in some situations, but being end-fed there is a high voltage at the end which is in the house. This may create EMC problems.

E

6. λ/4 vertical antennas

These have omni-directional radiation at a low angle. Impedance at the bottom of a λ/4 vertical antenna is 40–50Ω, and therefore it may be fed with 50Ω coaxial cable, the outer sheath of which is solidly earthed. The earthing arrangement is of paramount importance and, in most cases, a much more effective earth is a system of not less than three radial wires λ/4 long buried a few inches below the ground ('ground plane'). The radiator may be mounted on top of a mast with the guy wires acting as the earth (insulator in guy wires to limit electrical length to λ/4). Traps are often fitted for multi-band operation.

7. Low-frequency antennas

An effective resonant antenna for 1.8MHz is very long, hence shorter lengths tuned against earth may be used (the Marconi antenna). A very good earth (spike, not water pipe or mains earth) is required. Additional loading to compensate for very short lengths may be achieved by an inductance at outer end of antenna.

8. VHF and UHF antennas

Resonant antennas, as summarised above, are applicable to bands up to 1300MHz. The Yagi, and, to a lesser extent, the quad, are widely used. The shorter element length results in a much smaller antenna having many more elements than is practical at HF, and thus much higher antenna gain is achieved. To provide even higher gain, several such antennas can be matched and phased together ('stacked'). Feeder losses at these frequencies are much higher.

ERP and EIRP

Effective radiated power (ERP) in a given direction is the product of the power supplied to the antenna and the gain of the antenna (relative to a dipole). Used at frequencies below 1GHz.

Equivalent isotropically radiated power (EIRP) is the product of the power supplied to the antenna and the antenna gain, in a given direction, relative to an isotropic antenna. Used at frequencies above 1GHz.

Calculation of field strength

The calculation of field strength at a distant point is difficult. It is often useful in an EMC investigation to know the field strength at quite short distances. This can be estimated by the formula:

$$e = \frac{7.02 \sqrt{ERP}}{d}$$

where e is the field strength (peak) in volts per metre, d is the distance in metres from the transmitter, and the ERP is measured in watts.

7. TRANSMITTER INTERFERENCE

Interference caused can be classified as:

(a) interference to users of immediately adjacent frequencies;
(b) interference on frequencies which are much further away.

In either case interference may be caused at great distances. The amateur, therefore, has a great responsibility to ensure that his transmissions do not attract any criticism or break his licence conditions.

Defects can apply to home-constructed and commercial equipment, but top-grade commercial equipment should be free from defects unless caused by very occasional component faults or unofficial modification.

Frequency instability

The frequency of a VFO will vary if the mechanical stability of the circuit and components used is poor.

A slow change in frequency ('drift') occurs because some components in the oscillator change in value as the unit warms up, and thus stations in contact slowly drift apart, sometimes out of the band.

'Chirp' occurs as the morse key is closed. The usual reason is a badly regulated supply to the VFO which drops in value as more current is drawn from the supply. Chirp may also occur if the output and VFO frequencies are the same and feedback is occurring due to inadequate screening and filtering of the HT supply leads. Ideally the VFO should not be keyed and should be followed by an isolating stage.

Use of excessive bandwidth

It is accepted that the maximum bandwidth which need be transmitted for intelligible communication by speech is 300Hz to 2.5 or 3kHz. Therefore any transmission which is wider than this will cause interference with adjacent channels ('splatter'). Apart from this aspect, amateurs have a vested interest in the use of minimum bandwidth to permit more stations to operate in crowded bands. Amplitude modulation, having twice this bandwidth, is not acceptable on most amateur bands. Filtering of the bandwidth to the minimum occurs in SSB, but it is SSB which can produce the most serious interference in this category as the following diagram shows.

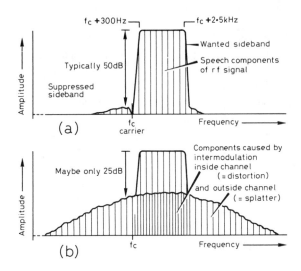

(a) represents the correctly adjusted signal. Maladjustment or attempts to 'talk the signal up' to obtain more power mean that the transmitter output stage or the following linear amplifier is overdriven to try and obtain a power output of which it is not capable. New unwanted signals are generated inside the transmitted channel (causing audible distortion) and outside the transmitted channel (causing splatter across adjacent frequencies). This situation is shown in diagram (b).

In an FM system the sidebands are infinitely wide, ie for an AF tone of 2.5kHz they will occur at ±5kHz and so on, but they can be neglected, providing the modulation index (the ratio of deviation to frequency of modulating signal) is less than 0.6. The design of the modulating circuits in an FM system is critical as regards the audio bandwidth and amplitude limiting of the FM input.

The break up of the carrier wave by 'over-modulation' in an AM system also creates interference.

A common aspect of all modulation systems is that over-modulation creates interference, but this situation is the result of maladjustment and so is under the control of the operator.

CW telegraphy

This is a form of amplitude modulation in which the carrier wave is switched on and off to form the morse characters. If the transition between the 'on/off' and 'off/on' states is too rapid, additional frequencies in the form of a short oscillatory waveform at each transition are created. The resultant 'key clicks' can be heard over a bandwidth of 100kHz or more over long distances, and may be worse if the transmitter power supply regulation is inadequate. Then the power transmitted surges over the first few per cent of each dot and dash. Thus 'key thumps' arise.

Key clicks are prevented by slowing up the rise and fall of the keyed waveform using a key-click filter. This consists of typically a 68Ω resistor in series with a 0.01μF capacitor across the key and a small inductor in series with the latter.

Unwanted transmitter outputs

Harmonics

These arise because amplifiers are to some degree non-linear, ie they distort the signal being amplified. This occurs particularly in high-power stages operating in Class C and to a lesser extent in Class AB linears. There may be leakage from frequency multipliers if these are used.

The closing of Band 1 TV has eliminated the main cause of complaints of amateur harmonic interference, but present and future users of the 41–68MHz band will be susceptible to this form of interference.

Standard remedies are pi output tuning in transmitter, adequate screening and filtering of leads, and a low-pass filter in the antenna lead.

The second or third harmonic of virtually every frequency in the HF amateur bands may possibly cause interference to someone somewhere.

Spurious oscillations

These are the result of unintentional feedback between the output and input of an amplifier which is generally caused by bad component layout, long leads, stray capacitance etc. The frequency does not necessarily coincide with the design frequency. Commercially any tendency to produce spurious responses should be designed out, but they may arise from such things as component failure or 'unofficial modification'. Listening to the amplifier on dummy load with a tuneable receiver is a convenient way to trace a suspected spurious response.

Mixer products

Modern amateur radio equipment depends entirely on the frequency mixing process to create the frequencies wanted. Almost inevitably unwanted frequencies can be generated.

These unwanted products are minimised by:

(a) careful choice of the signal generation and oscillator frequencies;
(b) use of balanced mixers to reduce the number of unwanted outputs;
(c) reduction of generation and mixing of harmonics by avoidance of over-drive of the mixer itself.

The synthesiser

The assumption that the design of the synthesiser in commercial equipment is satisfactory is entirely reasonable. Any spurious frequency detected which is thought to arise in the synthesiser circuits probably indicates a fault condition. The equipment should therefore be returned to the supplier for investigation.

Frequency measurement

Satisfactory means of frequency measurement must be available in the amateur station. (The DTI requirements should be noted.) Probably the most useful piece of ancillary equipment in the amateur station is a general-coverage receiver with means of checking its frequency calibration. This does not have to be the most up-to-date type!

8. ELECTROMAGNETIC COMPATIBILITY

"Electromagnetic compatibility is the ability of a device, equipment or system to function satisfactorily in its electromagnetic environment without introducing intolerable electromagnetic disturbances to anything in the environment".

EMC is clearly of immense importance in the current situation where there is increasing use of the RF spectrum and of consumer electronic equipment in particular. The responsibilities of the radio amateur are likewise increasing. The last section reviewed the ways in which any form of over-modulation of a radio transmitter can produce unwanted signals. Some of these may interfere with other radio amateurs, and the offender is hence likely to be informed quickly and sharply. It is interference to other services which is of most concern to amateur radio. How does this arise?

1. Radiation of wanted signals. Certain amateur bands are in the pass band of domestic equipment.
    (a) 1.8, 3.5 and possibly 7MHz may affect video-frequency circuits in TV and video recorders.
    (b) 3.5MHz may affect colour circuits (4.34MHz) of TVs.
    (c) 10.1MHz may affect 10.7MHz IF of FM receivers.

2. Radiation of unwanted signals (ie harmonics of wanted signals).
    (a) Harmonics of HF bands (1.8–30MHz) now of less significance since Band 1 TV ceased, but other services on 41–68MHz could be affected.
    (b) Third harmonic of 3.5MHz may affect 10.7MHz IF of FM receiver.
    (c) Third harmonic of top end of 28MHz may affect low end of Band 2 (FM), ie 87.5–89.1MHz.
    (d) Second harmonic of 50MHz band is 100–104MHz (Band 2 FM).
    (e) Fourth harmonic of 144MHz may affect channel 34 (TV).
    (f) Fifth harmonic of 144MHz may affect channels 52 and 53 (TV).

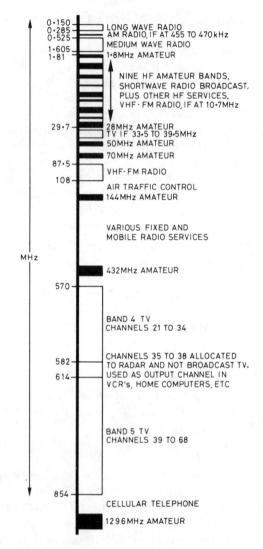

Reduce the occurrence of unwanted signals as follows:

1. Optimise station lay-out for good EMC.

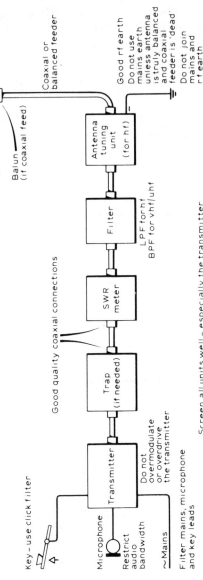

The above also applies basically to VHF and UHF, but trap and ATU may not be needed; the SWR meter is useful to check the integrity of the antenna system.

2. Position of antenna, particularly at HF, is important; an antenna in the roof space is likely to cause interference.

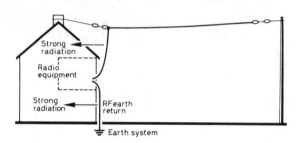

End fed not recommended

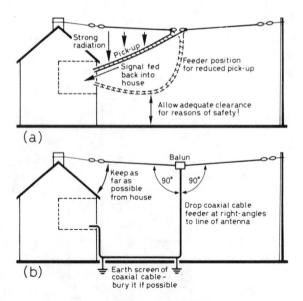

Avoid pick-up from antenna feeder

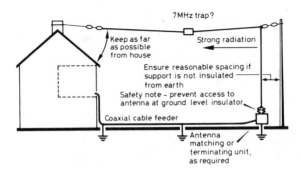

Fed at far end

Elimination/reduction of interfering signals

Domestic equipment likely to be affected:

(a) television receiver;
(b) video recorder;
(c) broadcast receiver (FM);
(d) broadcast receiver (M & L bands);
(e) audio equipment (hi-fi).

General notes

1. The term 'breakthrough' is increasingly used in this field. The difference between this and 'interference' can be thought of as follows: interference originates from a tuned RF source and affects a device via the tuned sections of its circuitry, eg receiver RF and/or IF stages. Breakthrough originates in the same way, but breaks through into untuned (ie broad-band) parts of the device, eg low-level early stages of an AF amplifier or long interconnecting leads in an AF amplifier system or a VCR. 'Breakthrough' is a less emotive term than 'interference' which tends to imply intent.

2. Modern domestic entertainment equipment is solid-state and assembled on printed circuit boards with minimum screening of circuits.

3. An EMC problem can disappear with even a slight reduction in

power level. It is not necessary to use maximum licensed power on every contact you make. In particular, note the ERP when maximum power at VHF or UHF is used if you have a multi-element stacked array.

Use of filters

Filtering of RF leads is the principal means of attenuating interfering signals. The types used are the low-pass, high-pass, band-pass and band-stop.

Typically a low-pass filter is used in the antenna lead of an HF band transmitter and a high-pass one in the antenna down lead of the receiver which is subject to interference. Band-stop and band-pass would be used with a 144MHz transmitter and a UHF TV receiver.

In practice, interfering signals from an HF transmitter are much more likely to break into a UHF TV via the outer braid of the TV antenna cable than be received via the TV antenna. The most likely cure is the braid-breaker.

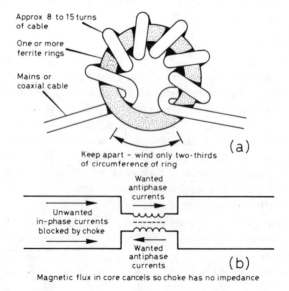

Approx 8 to 15 turns of cable

One or more ferrite rings

Mains or coaxial cable

Keep apart – wind only two-thirds of circumference of ring

(a)

Wanted antiphase currents

Unwanted in-phase currents blocked by choke

Wanted antiphase currents

(b)

Magnetic flux in core cancels so choke has no impedance

The braid-breaker can also be used where it is suspected that there is breakthrough via the mains lead of the TV.

Interference to radio receivers

Severe image interference could occur in the MW band from a 1.8MHz (160m) band transmission. It can also arise from the mixing of any frequency in the amateur bands with any frequency generated in the receiver mixer stage which will produce the intermediate frequency of the receiver. The 10.7MHz IF of the FM receiver is liable to interference from a 10.1MHz transmission or from the third harmonic of a 3.5MHz transmission. This situation does present a problem as most of the receivers in use are small, simple and have a built-in ferrite antenna. Avoidance of any spot frequencies which can be identified and power reduction are possible cures.

Interference to AF equipment

Generally arises from breakthrough of a strong local transmitter field into the early, low-level, broad-band stages of AF amplifiers or pick-up on to long interconnecting leads between amplifiers and speakers. These are probably the most common modes of interference and not the easiest to cure.

Interference to and from other equipment, such as VCR and computers etc, is a growing problem which may be minimised by fitting ring chokes to mains and other interconnecting leads.

Decoupling (0.001 to 0.01μF) at each end of interconnecting leads, ferrite beads or the braid-breaker (ferrite ring choke) technique are the likely answers to pick-up on long leads. Filtering or decoupling of the first transistor may be necessary, but this should not, for obvious reasons, be carried out by the radio amateur.

The social aspect of EMC

The newly licensed amateur is strongly advised not to use full power on all bands immediately – start gently and see what happens.

The irate neighbour demanding that something is done about that interference on his 'telly' is the most unwelcome visitor an amateur can have. While it may be tempting to reply in the same tone, this would be a grave tactical error, nor should the amateur try to browbeat the rather timid elderly lady into believing that it is all in her imagination.

It is essential that a friendly relationship is established from the start. Offer the visitor hospitality and show him your station. If you can demonstrate it in operation while your TV and hi-fi are in use, it will convince him that the problem is capable of solution.

At this stage it is better to use the term 'breakthrough' as it is less emotive! Several visits to his premises may be needed to appraise the situation, and the necessary action should then be fairly clear. If you are lucky, the trouble will be cured after the first visit by a braid-breaker or a filter or two, and a satisfactory agreement reached about fitting them and who pays for them.

Is further assistance needed?

There are a few situations where the amateur is unable to determine the mode of interference and hence cannot provide a cure, or where the complainant refuses to co-operate and starts a local campaign against the amateur and amateur radio in general which soon reaches the local press. If this should happen, the amateur (if he is an RSGB member) should contact the RSGB EMC Help Line (details in the *RSGB Amateur Radio Call Book*) and advise the complainant to refer the matter to the Radio Investigation Service of the DTI.

9. MEASUREMENTS

Accurate test equipment is needed to:

(a) confirm that the station is operating correctly;

(b) demonstrate compliance with the licence requirements.

DC measurements

The basis of all DC measurements is the moving-coil meter, commonly available with basic full-scale deflections (FSD) of about 25µA to about 10mA.

Current ranges are obtained by a resistor (the 'current shunt') across the meter. Voltage ranges are obtained by high-value resistors ('voltage multipliers') in series with the meter.

Voltmeter sensitivity is expressed in 'ohms per volt', eg if a 20,000Ω resistor is in series with a meter of FSD 5mA, it will be a 0–100V voltmeter. The current drawn at 100V is 5mA, and sensitivity is 20,000Ω/100V or 200Ω/V. Current taken by a voltmeter must not upset the circuit conditions, and the minimum preferred sensitivity is 20,000Ω/V.

AC measurements

The most accurate method is the moving-coil milliammeter used in conjunction with a meter rectifier (small bridge rectifier). Multiplier resistors may be added for voltage ranges; a current transformer is necessary for alternating current measurement (not commonly needed). May be used in the AF range.

Other AC instruments are:

Thermocouple. A moving-coil meter connected across a thermocouple, a junction of two dissimilar metals which is heated by the current to be measured. A thermocouple is easily burnt out. Reads RMS irrespective of waveform.

Electronic voltmeters consist of a diode detector followed by amplifier feeding a meter. Sensitivity is high (10MΩ) and maximum frequency may be 500MHz or so. Reads peak value, but calibrated in RMS.

There are likely to be errors in the measurement of alternating quantities if the waveform is not sinusoidal.

Transmitter measurements

1. Current measurement for tuning purposes. Maximise collector current by tuning input, tune collector circuit for minimum current, milliammeter of suitable range can be switched or plugged in.

2. PA input. Input is collector voltage multiplied by collector current. Collector current measured by permanently wired ammeter of suitable range (also essential for tuning). Collector voltage measured at input to PA (application of voltmeter to PA collector will throw PA off tune).

Dummy load

Essential for experimental work and transmitter tuning. It consists of a parallel arrangement of carbon resistors (non-inductive) with a value of 50–70Ω and a dissipation equal to the expected output of the transmitter. Lamps are not recommended as their resistance varies widely.

Frequency measurement

1. Standard crystal oscillator

The receiver can be calibrated by listening to the harmonics produced by a crystal oscillator. Accuracy depends on the mechanical integrity of the receiver dial and its logging arrangement. A 100kHz crystal is satisfactory at harmonics up to about 5MHz. Above this, a 1MHz crystal may be more convenient (depends on the amount of bandspread of the receiver).

2. Absorption wavemeter

Consists of a coil and variable capacitor in parallel. Absorbs power when held close to a tuned circuit at the same frequency. This is indicated by a sharp dip in the collector current associated with the tuned circuit under test. Useful for checking frequencies of transmitter tuned circuits, but is not very accurate, ie it will indicate top or bottom end of a band but not exact frequency. If combined with a rectifier, a meter and a short pick-up antenna (about 20cm), it will detect harmonics or spurious oscillators, but sensitivity is very low.

3. Dip meter
Consists of an oscillator using an FET. When the oscillator is tuned to the frequency of the tuned circuit under test (which does not have to be energised), power is absorbed from the oscillator which is indicated by the current dip. It has the same accuracy as the absorption wavemeter.

4. Digital frequency meter
This is the most accurate type. It utilises integrated circuits to count electronically the number of sine waves in a given period.

To simplify counting, the sine waves are converted to a train of square pulses. A 'clock' produces a series of pulses of known length (1s, 100ms, 10ms, 1ms etc) from a highly accurate crystal oscillator (1MHz or 5MHz). These pulses are used to open a 'gate' through which the converted waveform whose frequency is to be measured is allowed to pass. Thus the number of pulses in a period defined by the clock can be counted. The answer appears as a digital display.

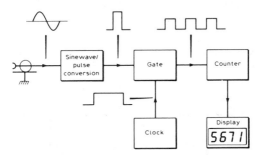

Modulation measurement
The breaking up of the carrier wave of an amplitude moderated transmission by over-modulation, ie greater than 100%, is likely to create interference in the immediate vicinity.

Modulated waveform can be displayed on a cathode-ray oscilloscope (CRO) so that modulation depth can be measured. The transmitter must be modulated by a constant tone (eg 1000Hz).

Typical CRO patterns (a) unmodulated current, (b) 50% modulation, (c) 100% modulation, (d) overmodulation are shown below.

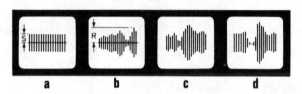

By measuring the peak amplitude of the modulation envelope R and the unmodulated carrier amplitude S as above, the modulation depth can be calculated:

$$\text{Depth} = \frac{R - S}{S} \times 100\%$$

SWR measurement

In an RF transmission line which is not properly matched, a proportion of the signal is reflected back along the line. The ratio of this 'reflected' power to the 'forward' power is related to the VSWR. Forward and reflected power can be shown on a reflectometer bridge.

Basic circuit of a simple reflectometer bridge (the Monimatch) is shown below:

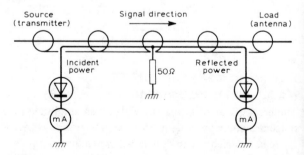

Incident power is shown on the left-hand meter and reflected power on the other. If a sensitivity control is used to enable the left-hand meter to be set to a calibration point, eg FSD, the reflected power meter can be calibrated in VSWR.

SSB power measurement

The conventional indicating meter cannot follow the syllabic variation in the current drawn by the output stage of an SSB transmitter. Hence the power dissipated in a dummy load is measured by a CRO (see overleaf).

Adjust power in the dummy load to 200W. This is equivalent to a PEP of twice this, ie 400W. Note the peak amplitude of this waveform by means of the CRO graticule or two thin lines drawn by chinagraph pencil on the tube face.

In use, the amplitude of the speech waveform shall not be allowed to exceed the amplitude defined by these lines.

Other power levels are determined as follows: if the deflection corresponding to 400W is 5cm and the deflection resulting from speech peaks is 2.5cm, the corresponding PEP is then:

$$400W \times \frac{2.5^2}{5^2} = 400W \times \left(\frac{2.5}{5}\right)^2$$

$$= 400W \times \left(\frac{1}{2}\right)^2 = 100W$$

Deflections are squared as they are proportional to the voltage which causes them, but power is proportional to voltage squared.

PEP can also be measured by a refined version of the Monimatch type of instrument which can be calibrated to measure power and PEP in addition to SWR.

Errors in measurement

A 'tolerance' is an indication of how accurate a meter is. A meter tolerance may be positive or negative and depends upon the type, age and previous history of the meter. Several tolerances affecting a reading can be added; this is likely to give a pessimistic answer.

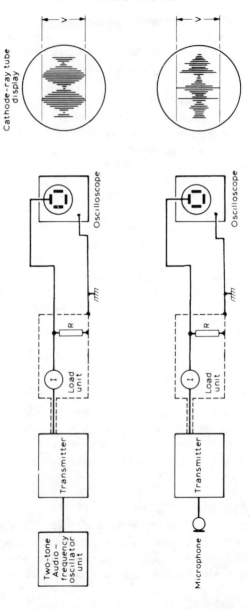

10. OPERATING PROCEDURES

Correct, and therefore considerate, operation is extremely important to avoid creating interference and to avoid giving the wrong impression of our hobby. This is particularly so when telephony is used and there is then a very much wider audience.

To establish communication

1. Listen on the chosen band for a few minutes in order to appraise propagation conditions.
2. Call a specific station, having netted on to his frequency, OR transmit a CQ call ('general invitation to reply'), having chosen a clear frequency.

Usually stations calling CQ can be heard, and hence the first alternative is often preferable.

Telephony procedures

Basic call

"WD9ZZZ. This is Golf Four Zulu Zulu Zulu calling, and Golf Four Zulu Zulu Zulu standing by".

CQ call

Before initiating a CQ, find a clear frequency.

"CQ CQ CQ. This is Golf Four Zulu Zulu Zulu calling CQ and standing by".

Net operation

Own callsign before each transmission, eg "from G4ZZZ", and at the end of transmission, indicate next station to transmit, eg

". . . WD4ZZZ to transmit. G4ZZZ in the group"

(Phonetic alphabet is not used.)

End of contact

"This is Golf Four Zulu Zulu Zulu signing clear with Whiskey Delta Nine Zulu Zulu Zulu. Golf Four Zulu Zulu Zulu is now standing by for a call" (or "is now closing down").

Both callsigns now given using the phonetic alphabet; indicate what is planned next.

"This is Golf Eight Zulu Zulu Zulu signing clear with Golf Two X-Ray Yankee Zulu mobile and now monitoring S20 for a call".

The importance of slow, clear enunciation of callsigns, using the recommended phonetic alphabet if necessary, cannot be over-stressed. Avoid:

(a) slang, jargon and clichés;
(b) pointless verbosity, eg "for any possible call", "K please", "K somebody please" etc;
(c) CW symbols, eg "hi hi", "dit dah dit dah dit" etc;
(d) Q-signals unless there is a language difficulty or heavy interference.

Telegraphy procedures

Basic call

G7AA G7AA G7AA de G7ZZ G7ZZ G7ZZ $\overline{\text{KN}}$

"$\overline{\text{KN}}$" means only G7AA to reply.

CQ call

Find a clear frequency.

CQ CQ CQ de G7ZZ G7ZZ G7ZZ K

"K" means any station to reply. Variants on the above are:

CQ DX CQ DX CQ DX de G7ZZ G7ZZ G7ZZ K
CQ VK CQ VK CQ VK de G7ZZ G7ZZ G7ZZ K

According to conditions, the calls may be sent up to three or four times.

"QRZ?" means "Who is calling me?", eg "QRZ de G7ZZ $\overline{\text{KN}}$" (note "$\overline{\text{KN}}$" now used). It is NOT an alternative to "CQ"; use it sparingly.

Do not repeat callsigns several times at end of each over; "$\overline{\text{AR}}$ G7ZZ de G7ZZ $\overline{\text{KN}}$" is all that is necessary.

Do not use every known farewell sign at the end of the QSO.

"hpe cuagn 73 es Dx. GB $\overline{VA}$" is sincere and surely says everything necessary. Do not follow "$\overline{VA}$" with another round of goodbyes and fervent promises to QSL!

Note:

$\overline{AR}$ – end of message or 'over'.

K – invitation to any station to reply.

$\overline{KN}$ – invitation to one particular station to reply.

$\overline{VA}$ – should only be used at the end of the final transmission in a QSO, ie the QSO is now finished and another station is justified in calling you on your frequency.

$\overline{CL}$ – I am closing down.

Avoid:

(a) sending faster than you can receive or than your contact is sending;

(b) using an automatic key on the air until sure that you can use it properly;

(c) sending double unless requested or your report is less than 339;

(d) prolonged CQ or specific calls;

(e) long and unnecessary phrases, eg "solid copy hr om" when "R" means just this!

General

The following apply equally to telephony and telegraphy.

1. Do not forget that some of the UK licence conditions are concerned with operation.

2. Always give honest reports – treat S-meter readings with reserve.

3. Band plans are not mandatory in the UK, but always observe them as they are in some countries and depend on licence class in others.

4. Always respect directional CQ calls.

5. Do not call anyone while he/she is in contact with another station.

6. Do not use DX bands for local contacts when they are open for long-distance working.
7. Move off a frequency at the end of a QSO if the station contacted was originally operating there.

The phonetic alphabet

The use of this and no other alphabet is particularly important. It is repeated here.

A	Alfa	J	Juliett	S	Sierra
B	Bravo	K	Kilo	T	Tango
C	Charlie	L	Lima	U	Uniform
D	Delta	M	Mike	V	Victor
E	Echo	N	November	W	Whiskey
F	Foxtrot	O	Oscar	X	X-ray
G	Golf	P	Papa	Y	Yankee
H	Hotel	Q	Quebec	Z	Zulu
I	India	R	Romeo		

Telegraphy codes

A great deal of amateur telegraphic communication depends upon symbols and abbreviations. There are literally hundreds of these which most amateurs will pick up quite quickly. A knowledge of all these is certainly not necessary for the RAE. The following symbols (Q-codes) may be used in the morse tests and are the most common. These should not be used in telephony unless conditions are bad or there is a language difficulty.

QRA QRG QRK QRL QRM QRN QRO QRP QRQ
QRS QRT QRV QRX QRZ QSB QSL QSO QSY
QTH

11. SAFETY PRECAUTIONS IN THE AMATEUR RADIO STATION

Safety precautions are essentially the appreciation of the hazards involved in a given situation and the application of common sense.

In amateur radio the hazard involved is in a particular use of electricity. Any voltage above 50V should be considered as dangerous. Much equipment now operates from a 13.5V supply at up to about 30A, which is usually obtained from the 240V mains. Earlier transmitters are likely to include a supply of about 800V, while linear amplifiers using valves operate at about 2000V. This is certainly lethal.

All mains supplies to amateur equipment (work bench included) must be adequately insulated, fused and switched, with all cases and exposed metalwork properly earthed. All power outlets in the station should be controlled by a master switch, the function and position of which should be known to all in the house. The implications of PME must be understood – if not, it is essential that they are discussed with the local Electricity Board.

A few obvious rules:

1. Switch off and disconnect before removing the covers.
2. Do not wear headphones whilst delving inside.
3. Remember that high-value capacitors will hold a significant charge. The high-voltage paper capacitor (4mF, 2500V) will hold a charge (possibly fatal) for a long time. All such capacitors should be fitted with a parallel-bleed resistor.
4. Confirm (c) – if negative, discharge all such capacitors with an insulated and earthed wand.
5. If the floor is damp, stand on a rubber mat.

Mobile operation

1. The mechanical integrity of all equipment and the mountings thereof, both inside and outside the car, shall be such that there is no possibility of their becoming loose in the event of sudden braking or an accident. In particular the antenna (maximum

length 14ft) shall not be capable of flexing at speed and endangering other cars or pedestrians.

2. Driver shall not use a hand microphone or make any adjustments (eg tuning) while in motion.

3. All equipment shall be switched off when (i) refuelling; (ii) when close to petrol tanks; or (iii) when near quarries where explosives are detonated electrically.

4. A fire extinguisher shall be readily accessible.

RF hazards

It is generally agreed that the only biologically significant property of RF energy is in heating and is only a hazard if the heat is not removed by the body's temperature-regulating mechanism.

The level accepted in UK for continuous exposure to RF is set at 10mW/cm. This level is unlikely to be met with in amateur radio in the UK.

Microwave radiation in itself is not more hazardous, but the smaller area over which microwaves are likely to radiate results in a greater power density.

Situations to be avoided:

1. Do not look down a waveguide unless you know that there is no RF at the other end.

2. Do not work on high-power RF equipment with the covers off. (There is probably high voltage present as well!)

3. Do not use an unscreened dummy load or a small antenna in the shack for test purposes.

4. Do not adjust antennas using full power.

5. Do not use a hand-held set without using a thick insulating cap on the end of the antenna.

6. Hold the hand-held set so that the antenna is as far as possible from the face.

12. LICENCE CONDITIONS

Candidates are referred to *How to Become a Radio Amateur* for current conditions. The principal headings are listed below.

1. Use of an amateur radio station.
2. Location of the station, main and temporary addresses, mobile, maritime mobile.
3. Limitations on use.
4. Qualifications of operators.
5. Limits of principal bands, primary and secondary use, powers permitted.
6. Permitted types of emission.
7. Callsigns and their use for identification, prefix to be used in other parts of UK, use of /P, /M, /MM. Club stations and GB calls.
8. Frequency control and measurement.
9. Avoidance of interference.
10. Antenna location.
11. Log keeping.
12. Inspection.
13. Licence, fees, duration etc.

13. SUMMARY OF FORMULAE

Ohm's Law $\quad R = \dfrac{V}{I} \quad V = IR \quad I = \dfrac{V}{R}$

Power $\quad W = V \times I \quad W = I^2 R \quad W = \dfrac{V^2}{R}$

Reactance $\quad X_L = 2\pi f L$

$$X_C = \dfrac{1}{2\pi f C}$$

Resonance $\quad f_r = \dfrac{1}{2\pi\sqrt{LC}}$

Resistors (series) $\quad R = R_1 + R_2 + R_3 + \ldots$

Resistors (parallel) $\quad \dfrac{1}{R} = \dfrac{1}{R_1} + \dfrac{1}{R_2} + \dfrac{1}{R_3} + \ldots$

Two resistors (parallel) $\quad R = \dfrac{R_1 \times R_2}{R_1 + R_2}$

$$= \dfrac{\text{product}}{\text{sum}}$$

Capacitors (series) $\quad \dfrac{1}{C} = \dfrac{1}{C_1} + \dfrac{1}{C_2} + \dfrac{1}{C_3} + \ldots$

Capacitors (parallel) $\quad C = C_1 + C_2 + C_3 + \ldots$

Two capacitors (series) $\quad C = \dfrac{C_1 \times C_2}{C_1 + C_2}$

$$= \dfrac{\text{product}}{\text{sum}}$$

$\lambda/2$ antenna (in space) $= \dfrac{150}{f(\text{MHz})}$

$\lambda/2$ antenna (practical) $= \dfrac{143}{f(\text{MHz})}$

Wavelength (metres) $= \dfrac{300}{f(\text{MHz})}$

$$Q = \frac{\omega L}{R}$$

$$R_{\text{D}} = \frac{L}{CR} \quad \text{and since} \quad Q = \frac{\omega L}{R}$$

$$R_{\text{D}} = \frac{Q}{\omega C}$$

$$Q = \frac{f_{\text{r}}}{f_{\text{h}} - f_{\text{l}}}$$

Energy in capacitor (joules) $= \frac{1}{2}CV^2$

RMS value of sine wave $= 0.707 \times$ peak
Average value of sine wave $= 0.636 \times$ peak

$$e = \frac{7.02\,\sqrt{\text{ERP}}}{d}$$

where e is the field strength (peak) in volts per metre, d is the distance in metres from the transmitter, and the ERP is measured in watts.

Approximations

$\pi \approx 3.14$ or $22/7$ $\qquad \sqrt{2} \approx 1.41$
$\pi^2 \approx 10$ $\qquad\qquad\qquad \sqrt{3} \approx 1.73$
$1/\pi \approx 0.32$ $\qquad\qquad\quad \sqrt{5} \approx 2.24$
$1/2\pi \approx 0.16$ $\qquad\qquad\quad \sqrt{10} \approx 3.162$

Quantity	Symbol used in formulae	Unit	Abbreviation
Current	I	ampere	A
EMF	E	volt	V
Electric potential	V	volt	V
Time	t	second	s
Resistance	R	ohm	Ω
Capacitance	C	farad	F
Inductance	L	henry	H
Mutual inductance	M	henry	H
Power	W	watt	W
Frequency	f	hertz (one cycle per second)	Hz
Wavelength	λ	metre	m

Abbrevations for multiples and sub-multiples

G	giga	10^9
M	mega	10^6
k	kilo	10^3
c	centi	10^{-2}
m	milli	10^{-3}
μ	micro	10^{-6}
n	nano	10^{-9}
p	pico	10^{-12}